SELF. CENTERED.

A 30-Day Guided Journey to Radical,
Unapologetic, Life-Affirming Self-Love

By TENIQUA POPE

THIS JOURNAL BELONGS TO:

Contents

Who Is This Journey For?

This guided journey is for you if you dare to *thrive despite the chaos*. You have the audacity to prioritize self-care because of everything going on around you. You know that all your growing pains are never in vain if you've gleaned the lessons they produce. Here, you will practice acknowledging, embracing, and caring for your whole self, growing past doubt and regret, and aligning yourself with your inner vision for your life.

Introduction

I don't know who needs to hear this, but the perfect life plan is a myth. There is no magic, one-size-fits-all journal, app, therapist, retreat... no perfect anything to help you get your life to where you want it to be. Your existence is a series of resets. Committing, then stopping. Trying, failing, then trying again – with someone, something, somewhere else.

Now, consider that we're all pressing the reset (and panic) button at the same time during a global pandemic, a civil rights movement, and seemingly non-stop natural disasters, all in the throes of a historic presidential election. Our pursuit of the ever-elusive "new normal" forces a reckoning with some of our outdated ideals and an acceptance of some very hard truths about ourselves and everything we've accepted as ordinary.

True self-awareness is an act of self-love, and you certainly don't need anyone's permission to love yourself. What I offer here instead is this space for you to become intimately reacquainted with yourself. In this journey, you'll find introspective writing prompts and writing spaces for your realest, most transparent responses.

You already have the blueprint for your success within you. Use this journey to hold space for yourself, sort through your triumphs and missteps, and sift out the gems that sustained you at your low points and inspired you in your highs.

Pre-Assessment

Before you get started, let's take inventory of your self-awareness.
You will retake this assessment at the end of the journey and note your progress.

Rate how accurate these statements are for you on a scale of 1 to 10.
(1 - not at all; 10 - very accurate.)

_____ I have clarity around exactly who I am.

_____ I have healthy coping skills to deal with everyday stress.

_____ I know what I want out of life.

_____ I know how to get what I want out of life.

_____ I have a solid plan and I've taken action to get what I want out of life.

_____ I have personal and professional goals that excite me.

_____ I can list 5 things that I enjoy about life.

_____ I have healthy relationships with men and women.

_____ I have a consistent self-care regimen.

_____ Who I am on the inside is accurately expressed in how I show up in the world.

_____ I make positive and memorable first impressions.

_____ I know how to make and keep friends.

_____ I am congruent to who I am in all areas of my life and with everyone in it.

_____ I am comfortable asking for what I want.

_____ I know what I have to offer.

WEEK ONE

Love yourself more *each day*. If you fall out of love with yourself, devote yourself to returning to that love. You cannot abandon yourself. Take care of yourself. Forgive yourself. Embrace your flaws and don't abuse others with them. Celebrate your greatness without making anyone feel less than. Be completely enamored with the person you are becoming.

DAY 1 - AM

In order to make room in your life for the things you desire, you have to first make room for yourself. Reserve time at the beginning and end of your day just to pray, practice self-care, set goals, and conquer! Write down your self-care routine and what time each day you plan to devote to yourself on this journey.

My self-care routine: _____

_____

_____

_____

_____

_____

_____

_____

_____

_____

_____

I will practice my self-care routine at:

_____ AM/PM

DAY 1 - PM

Set aside time to rest and meditate. Often, the world around us, and even the voice in our own head, is so loud that we cannot hear the universe call. Dim the lights. Unplug your devices and settle into the most restful sleep you can imagine. Hold this page open with a pen at your bedside so you can write down what is revealed to you tonight.

DAY 2 - AM

Unlike a product that you can purchase online or at a store, human beings do not come with instructions for care. Instead, it is usually through the act of simply living that we get to know what foods, people, locations, and experiences help us function at our best.

Think about your life. What good things refresh you?

What things deplete you?

In the space below, write down instructions for your care as if you were delivering the note to someone you trust to care for you.

DAY 2 - PM

What does it mean for you to be confidently you? What old ways of thinking or past hurts or disappointments are getting in the way of your confidence?

DAY 3 - AM

Choose to love yourself
first. *How will you love
yourself today?*

DAY 3 - PM

Having a consistent, faithful, and positive support system is crucial to achieving what feels impossible. Who in your life supports and encourages you? List those people below and commit to celebrating with and leaning on them during this time.

1

2

3

4

5

DAY 4 - AM

Take time to check in with yourself and keep track of your emotions. Emotions are
just outward expressions of what's going on within your heart. What was the first
thing on your mind this morning? Why do you think that is?

DAY 4 - PM

Friendly reminder (because we all get busy and forget) to grab your phone and make appointments with yourself, for yourself. Commit to waking up 30 minutes earlier and going to bed 30 minutes later to give yourself time alone to pamper, pray or meditate, and plan. Write down what time each day you plan to devote to yourself and this journey. If you've already completed this step on Day 1, use the space below to write about how it's going so far.

I will practice my self-care routine at:

_____ AM/PM

SELF. CENTERED.

DATE   /   /

DAY 5 - AM

You control your own
narrative. *What do you
say about yourself?*

15

DAY 5 - PM

Your thoughts set the tone for your days
and your days set the course for your life.

How is your *life?*

How are your *days?*

How are your *thoughts?*

DAY 6 - AM

Indulge yourself in people, objects, and experiences that remind you of how
wonderful you are. List the loved ones, places, treasures, etc. that make you feel
radiant in the space below.

1. ....

2. ....

3. ....

4. ....

5. ....

6. ....

7. ....

8. ....

9. ....

10. ....

11. ....

12. ....

13. ....

14. ....

15. ....

DAY 6 - PM

What do you need more of today?

_____

_____

_____

_____

_____

_____

_____

What must you release to receive it?

_____

_____

_____

_____

_____

DAY 7 - AM

Take some time to check in with
yourself and recharge for the
week ahead. *What worked well
for you this week? How can you
incorporate those things into your
daily routine?*

DAY 7 - PM

Review your journal entries from the week and set a powerful intention for yourself based on what you've discovered. Write your intention in the space below, then share your intention with the three people closest to you who will support your vision and hold you accountable. Write their names below and check them off after you've spoken with them.

My intention for the upcoming week:

WEEK TWO

The times are always uncertain. None of us have inerrant insight into the future or the power to change anything from our pasts. Your ability to adjust is directly proportional to your ability to ascend. *Comfort cannot coexist with breakthroughs.* If your fingers remain clenched around the familiar, you may miss the opportunity to grasp greatness. Uncertain or not, now is the time to align yourself with your aspirations.

DAY 8 - AM

Take a break from social media and the virtual world and connect with yourself in
silence and mindful movements like walking, stretching, or dance.

How do you feel?

_____

_____

_____

_____

_____

_____

_____

_____

_____

_____

_____

_____

_____

_____

_____

DAY 8 - PM

Take time to clear the clutter in your living space. Even positive possessions and activities can be a distraction if they do not fit with who you are right now and where you're trying to go.

What are the hardest things to let go of?

1. ....

2. ....

3. ....

4. ....

5. ....

6. ....

7. ....

What voids did you discover?

DAY 9 - AM

Think of one special little thing that you can do for yourself every day and one luxurious thing that you can save for the weekend. Write down your ideas below and commit to prioritizing acknowledging, nourishing, and replenishing yourself.

❋ ....

❋ ....

❋ ....

❋ ....

❋ ....

❋ ....

❋ ....

❋ ....

❋ ....

DAY 9 - PM

Saying no and setting boundaries is an integral part of self-care.

What do you need to say no to?

_____

_____

_____

_____

_____

_____

How does that make you feel?

_____

_____

_____

_____

_____

_____

DAY 10 - AM

_____

_____

_____

_____

_____

_____

_____

_____

_____

_____

_____

_____

_____

Practice listening to yourself.
What is your body telling you?
Your mind? Your spirit?

DAY 10 - PM

Wanting your needs met does not make you needy. When a need arises within you (for food, attention, release, etc.) unapologetically attend to those needs. There are no medals for endurance or self-denial. Distinguish wisely between a want and a need and then don't let anything or anyone (not even yourself through sloth or guilt or over-analysis) stop you from getting your needs met.

What did you need more of today?

_____

_____

_____

_____

_____

_____

_____

_____

_____

_____

_____

DAY 11 - AM

Move your body this morning. Stretch. Dance. Sing while you are getting ready for the day. How do you feel?

DAY 11 - PM

Take time to check in with yourself and keep track of your emotions. Emotions are just outward expressions of what's going on within your heart.

How are you feeling without the things you've given up?

What do you want back?

What are you happier without?

DAY 12 - AM

Keep moving. Get up a little earlier if you can. Set the tone and claim today for yourself. What mindfulness movement(s) will you add to your morning routine?

❋ _____

❋ _____

❋ _____

❋ _____

❋ _____

❋ _____

❋ _____

❋ _____

❋ _____

❋ _____

DAY 12 - PM

How do you take care of yourself after a difficult day?

_____

_____

_____

_____

_____

_____

_____

Are those habits and coping skills in alignment with who you are becoming?

_____

_____

_____

_____

_____

_____

DAY 13 - AM

Go outside today. If you are able, explore your neighborhood, a park, or a trail. Or just sit outside with some ambient music and lime water. *How do you feel when you connect with nature?*

DAY 13 - PM

If the great outdoors isn't so great to you, spend time creating a healing space in your home. What things will you bring to that space?

* _____

* _____

* _____

* _____

* _____

* _____

* _____

* _____

* _____

* _____

DAY 14 - AM

You're probably well overdue for a recharge. Rest today.

Write down what you did today to relax and replenish.

DAY 14 - PM

With every act of self-care, your highest self is edified and your inner critic is
silenced. Do you feel stronger? Review your journal entries from the week and set
a powerful intention for yourself based on what you've discovered.

Write your intention in the space below and share it with those who lift you up
and keep you grounded.

WEEK THREE

How to Boost Your Emotional IQ

- **Share** your thoughts with a trusted friend, life coach, or mental health professional.

- **Journal** daily to process and track emotions on your own.

- **Avoid** responding in anger or hurt.

- **Set** boundaries and embrace the power of "no."

- **Build** self-care rituals and rewards into your weekly routine.

- **Remove** yourself from unhealthy situations.

- **Replenish** yourself daily with affirmations.

- **Manage** your emotions.

- **Feed** your thoughts.

- **Control** your actions.

DAY 15 - AM

When you are not obsessed with preserving who others think you are, you are free to become who you need and want to be. Use the space below to describe the person you desire to become.

_____

_____

_____

_____

_____

_____

_____

_____

_____

_____

_____

_____

_____

_____

DAY 15 - PM

What did you grow up believing about yourself
that you now know just wasn't true?

_____

_____

_____

_____

_____

_____

How does that belief from your childhood affect how you view yourself today?

_____

_____

_____

_____

_____

_____

_____

DAY 16 - AM

Affirm yourself this morning with 5 things
that you absolutely adore about yourself.

1

2

3

4

5

DAY 16 - PM

Think of a habit that you may have embraced as a child or during a trial that no longer serves you. Give yourself grace and encouragement for your ingenuity and drive to create coping strategies to get through tough times. *Now take that same resourceful creativity to craft a personal care routine worthy of where you are now.*

DAY 17 - AM

What's the best thing that happened so far this week?

DAY 17 - PM

What does it mean for you to master yourself?

*Commit right now to get to the heart of who you really are
and discover what you need to feel fulfilled and aligned with
your unique version of happiness.*

DAY 18 - AM

Just breathe. Put on some nature sounds, jazz, classical, or some other music (preferably without lyrics) and just breathe. Write whatever comes to mind.

DAY 18 - PM

Check in with yourself. *What
have you learned this past week?*

DAY 19 - AM

Get to know yourself and accept what you discover.

How would *you* describe yourself?

How would your *parents* describe you?

How would your *friends* describe you?

How would your *co-workers* describe you?

DAY 19 - PM

Was there an incident or conversation this week that triggered you?

_____

_____

_____

_____

What situations brought you peace?

_____

_____

_____

_____

Which ones caused you anxiety?

_____

_____

_____

_____

DAY 20 - AM

Take inventory of your schedule. Are you super busy? Bored from lack of involvement in anything that excites you? What's on your mind today?

_____

_____

_____

_____

_____

_____

_____

_____

_____

_____

_____

_____

_____

DAY 20 - PM

On a separate sheet of paper, dump any negative messages floating through your mind today that are causing you to feel less than. Now rip that paper into the smallest, most insignificant pieces you can and throw it away. *In the space above, write about what needs your attention right now.*

DAY 21 - AM

Pick one of the indulgent (yet mindful) activities
you listed on Day 9 and give yourself a mini-retreat.

How does that make you feel?

_____

_____

_____

_____

_____

_____

_____

_____

_____

_____

_____

_____

DAY 21 - PM

What lessons from this week do you want to take into the next? Set and write
your intention below and again on a sticky note to put on your bathroom mirror as
a daily reminder of the amazing experiences to come.

WEEK FOUR

7 Practical Ways to Take Ownership of Your Day

1. **Awaken** slowly.
2. **Scan** your body and mind.
3. **Address** any low energy manifestations.
4. **Set** your intention for the day.
5. **Drink** lime water.
6. **Stretch** for 30 minutes.
7. **Connect** and share joy.

DAY 22 - AM

Prepare to be amazed. What amazing life experiences are you looking forward to?

DAY 22 - PM

The key word in this morning's prompt: prepare. If you want something, anything, then prepare to receive it. If you don't prepare, the universe will determine that you are not ready. Prepare to be amazed and something amazing will be revealed. *How will you prepare your mind, body, and spirit to receive what you are after?*

DAY 23 - AM

Put on your favorite song and sing and dance like no one's watching. If that's too much, maybe put on some headphones and lip-sync your heart out. Write your thoughts about this activity below.

DAY 23 - PM

Your responses to life events mold you. You mold yourself. You control yourself.
Even amid chaos. So, while life events may be beyond your control, your life
experience is completely up to you.

Take some time to visualize the life you want to lead. Use the space on the next
few pages to capture those thoughts. Feel free to use words, magazine clippings,
sketches, quotes, etc.

DAY 24 - AM

What are you most proud of this week?

DAY 24 - PM

What are some of the obstacles (real or perceived) that stand in the way of the full manifestation of your desires?

❀ _____

❀ _____

❀ _____

❀ _____

❀ _____

❀ _____

❀ _____

❀ _____

❀ _____

❀ _____

DAY 25 - AM

What are the top 3 things you want to accomplish today? Write them below.
Before you leave your bedroom to start your day, sit quietly and visualize yourself
getting these tasks done.

1

2

3

DAY 25 - PM

Did you complete your tasks for the day?

If so, what helped? If not, what stood in the way?

Align yourself with the vision living within.

DAY 26 - AM

There is room for you. Your ambition. Your sensibility. Your swagger. You do not need validation or adornment. You exist to radiate the light already living in you. Describe that light in the space below.

DAY 26 - PM

What things, people, or happenings cause you to shine brightest?

_____

_____

_____

_____

_____

_____

_____

What dims your light?

_____

_____

_____

_____

_____

_____

_____

DAY 27 - AM

_____

_____

_____

_____

_____

_____

_____

_____

_____

_____

_____

_____

_____

Rest. Replenish. Release.
*Then capture your
thoughts here.*

_____

_____

DAY 27 - PM

What is the main reason you started this journey?

_____

_____

_____

_____

_____

_____

Have you made the progress that you were hoping to? Why or why not?

_____

_____

_____

_____

_____

_____

DAY 28 - AM

The origin, purpose, and destination of your journey exist in your heart, in your mind, and in your spirit. Describe your personal journey.

DAY 28 - PM

Now that you've gotten some clarity on who you are, it becomes easier to tune out the world's chatter (societal expectations, norms, standards, etc.) and tune in to your own desires.

What amazing life experiences are you looking forward to?

How can you prepare to receive them?

Pursue what brings you joy.
No amount of someone else's joy will ever satisfy you.

DAY 29 - AM

Go to your happy place, either outside or the healing space you created within your home, and just enjoy your own company. What thoughts come to mind?

_____

_____

_____

_____

_____

_____

_____

_____

_____

_____

_____

_____

_____

DAY 29 - PM

Discipline is the foresight and maturity to adhere to your own helpful habits, schedules, and routines regardless of how you feel in the moment. It exists independent of inspiration and breeds productivity in the absence of internal motivation.

Where do you lack motivation or accountability?

What would you say is the block?

Who or what resources can help you remove the block and keep moving forward?

DAY 30 - AM

Words have power. Your own words guide your fate.

What will you tell yourself today to perpetuate courage
and inspiration beyond this journey?

DAY 30 - PM

Now that you're tuning out the world's chatter — tune in to your own heart and solidify your "why." *Why are your goals important to you right now? What will your life be like when you have mastered these things? Who will you become?*

Post-Assessment

Please retake the inventory of your self-awareness by rating how accurate these statements are for you on a scale of 1 to 10. (1 - not at all; 10 - very accurate.)

Compare your first score to this one. What do you notice?

_____ I have clarity around exactly who I am.

_____ I have healthy coping skills to deal with everyday stress.

_____ I know what I want out of life.

_____ I know how to get what I want out of life.

_____ I have a solid plan and I've taken action to get what I want out of life.

_____ I have personal and professional goals that excite me.

_____ I can list 5 things that I enjoy about life.

_____ I have healthy relationships with men and women.

_____ I have a consistent self-care regimen.

_____ Who I am on the inside is accurately expressed in how I show up in the world.

_____ I make positive and memorable first impressions.

_____ I know how to make and keep friends.

_____ I am congruent to who I am in all areas of my life and with everyone in it.

_____ I am comfortable asking for what I want.

_____ I know what I have to offer.

About the Author

Teniqua Pope is a dynamic, holistic life coach, mediator, and mentor. She has guided many wonderful women (and a handful of amazing men) on their paths to self-love and emotional wellness. *Self. Centered.* captures her unique, results-driven coaching style in a structured, self-paced journal format that's user-friendly, engaging, and effective.

Teniqua created this paradigm-shifting journey of self-love for people, like herself, who need the occasional reminder to slow down and fill up before pouring into the countless people and passion projects that live in their hearts. Applying the principles of self-care, self-love, self-awareness, and self-alignment to her own life liberated her in her battles with depression, imposter syndrome, and fear of failure.

Teniqua works full-time in local government, volunteers her coaching skills for low-income, at-risk adults, co-leads a women's empowerment group, and is a recent convert to the minimalist movement in Denver.